THE MOXA IN MOTION
COLOURING
AND WORKBOOK

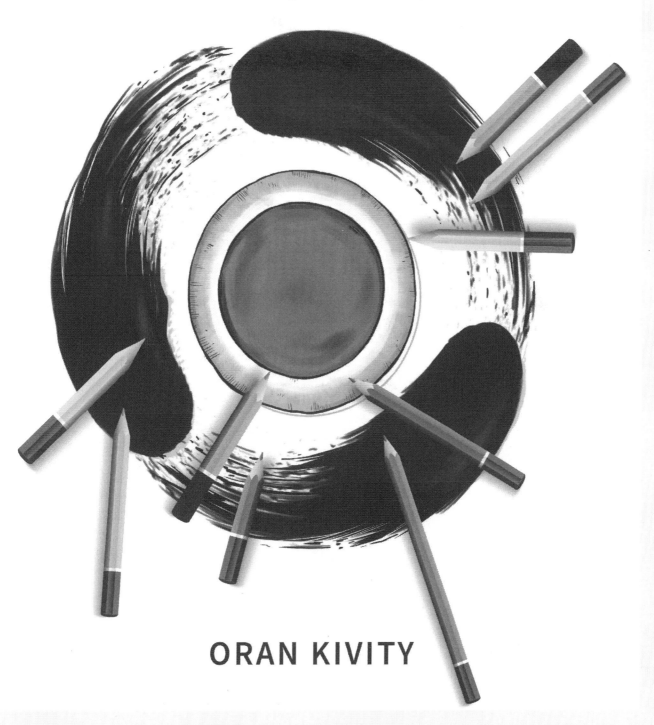

ORAN KIVITY

Cover Design: Jietwong.com
Illustrations: Vio Lau

A NOTE FROM THE AUTHOR

WELCOME TO THIS COLOURING BOOK

Welcome to *The Moxa in Motion Colouring and Workbook*. It is designed to help you get to grips with the information in its partner book *Moxa in Motion with the Ontake Method.* The structure mirrors the sections and chapters of the main book and comprises worksheets, diagrams and exercises to help you get a handle on the material. In addition, the book is generously laced with barcodes that you can scan with your phone to bring you to time-coded videos on YouTube that demonstrate many of the techniques or concepts.

Many of the questions are multiple-choice. Just put a mark next to the correct answer. Other questions are more reflective, requiring you to look up the answer in the main book and formulate it for yourself. Other exercises will require you to colour in diagrams or send you to YouTube so that you can practise while watching.

The main book was written in the hope that you would read it chapter by chapter but in the expectation that you wouldn't! Some of the concepts may seem elementary to you, in which case you will naturally be tempted to skip from one part to another. Even if that is the case, I suggest that you try to complete the worksheets and exercises in sequence. If you can't answer any of the questions, it might be good for you to return to the relevant chapter in the main book.

On the last pages of this book, there's a list of resources, including links to the YouTube channel and Facebook group, as well as my author's landing page. Here you can learn more about group and individual coaching, and online and in-person teaching to help you on your Ontake journey.

Happy tapping!

Oran Kivity

Oran Kivity
Kaohsiung, Taiwan, 2021

LEARNING GOALS

As a teacher of Ontake, I'd like to share with you my hopes for your learning goals. By the time you reach the end of this book, I want you to feel competent and confident about using Ontake in your practice. So here are some very specific goals. Tick each one that you want to achieve.

☐ I WILL KNOW HOW TO LOAD, LIGHT, CHECK AND EXTINGUISH ONTAKE

☐ I WILL BE ABLE TO APPLY A VARIETY OF DIFFERENT STROKES

☐ I WILL BE ABLE TO USE A METRONOME TO APPLY THESE STROKES AT DIFFERENT FREQUENCIES

☐ I'LL BE ABLE TO TREAT ANY PART OF THE BODY SAFELY, INCLUDING THE FACE

☐ I'LL BE ABLE TO USE ONTAKE FOR PAIN RELIEF

Do you have any goals you want to add? Write them down in the spaces below.

PART ONE

THE BASICS

CHAPTER ONE
ONTAKE ORIGINS

THE KEY CONCEPTS OF THIS CHAPTER

- A history of Ontake
- Introducing Dr Manaka
- The evolution of the Ontake Method

WORKSHEET ONE (1)

INSTRUCTIONS: Answer the worksheet questions below.

1. Which one of the following statements is correct?

☐ Bamboo moxibustion has been around since the sixteenth-century Mubunryu school

☐ Zuiho Ito may have been the first to use bamboo moxibustion in the 1960s or 70s

☐ Oran Kivity created this moxibustion tool in 2009

☐ Sankei acupuncture suppliers were the first to import these tools from China

2. Which one of the following statements is correct?

☐ Ontake moxibustion is a new term for bamboo tube moxibustion

☐ Ontake moxibustion is a new term for bamboo ring moxibustion

☐ "*On*" means warm, "*take*" means bamboo

☐ All of the above

☐ None of the above

WORKSHEET ONE (2)

3. Which of the following describe Dr Manaka accurately?

☐ He was a medical doctor who combined research with an interest in traditional methods

☐ He developed a percussive style of treatment using a wooden hammer and needle

☐ He was a mentor and guide for Stephen Birch, who co-authored *Chasing the Dragon's Tail* in English

☐ All of the above

☐ None of the above

4. Which one of the following support the statement that all moxibustion is cyclical?

☐ It's good to have moxibustion from time to time

☐ Moxa sticks are cylindrical, so they roll back and forward

☐ Life is a balance between yin and yang and hot and cold

☐ Lighting, extinguishing and replacing moxa cones creates a cycle of warmth and coolness

5. Which of the following do you agree with?

☐ Bamboo is a pressing and rolling tool that can be applied with Dr Manaka's wooden hammer

☐ Applying heat with Ontake is fraught with difficulties

☐ Ontake cannot be pressed on the skin without insulating material

☐ Combining moxibustion with Dr Manaka's meridian frequencies broadens the range and scope of both

WORKSHEET ONE (3)

6. Write down at least two things that you learnt from this chapter in the spaces below. These could be observations, learning tips or any other kind of "note-to-self".

CHAPTER TWO
GETTING STARTED

THE KEY CONCEPTS OF THIS CHAPTER

- Sourcing bamboo
- Terminology
- Loading and lighting bamboo
- Clinic hygiene

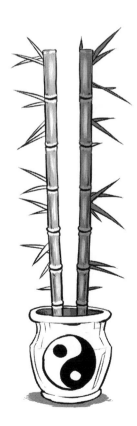

WORKSHEET TWO (1)

INSTRUCTIONS: Answer the worksheet questions below.

1. Using the diagram below, mark in the dimensions of a standard-sized Ontake.

2. Add the following labels to the diagram: mouth, shaft, skin, lip, bore, plug, base.

WORKSHEET TWO (2)

LOADING & LIGHTING

3. Use your phone to scan the time-coded barcode above. It links to a video on YouTube on how to load and light Ontake (free webinar with the *Journal of Chinese Medicine*). Practise with your own Ontake during the lesson.

4. Which one of the following statements is true?

☐ Packing the plug tightly so it won't move helps it breathe

☐ Packing the plug loosely feels comfortable when you put your fingers inside the bamboo

☐ Packing the plug tightly is necessary so that it doesn't fall out of the bamboo when you're working

☐ The more you use the bamboo, the more tightly you have to pack the plug

WORKSHEET TWO (3)

5. Which one of the following statements is true?

☐ A long plug is better than a short one

☐ A short plug is better than a long one

☐ A short plug is better for practitioners with sensitive hands

☐ The longer the plug, the cooler the burn

6. Which one of the rules below is correct for loading mini-Ontake?

☐ Load the same as for standard Ontake

☐ Compress the plug to the centre of the bamboo, so the plug is well away from the edge

☐ Load the same as for super-Ontake, so the plug takes up 40% of the bamboo

☐ Load from both ends until it's full

7. Which of the following options will ensure the best clinic hygiene?

☐ Have an ample supply of Ontake to use throughout the day

☐ Use one Ontake per patient

☐ Use a UV steriliser at the end of the day

☐ All of the above

WORKSHEET TWO (4)

8. List three approaches to reloading the Ontake with moxa (see p. 15).

9. Write down at least two things that you learnt from this chapter in the spaces below. These could be observations, learning tips or any other kind of "note-to-self".

CHAPTER THREE
REGULATION

THE KEY CONCEPTS OF THIS CHAPTER

- The idea of regulation
- Introducing Dr Manaka's octahedral model
- Reviewing key acupuncture concepts from a Japanese perspective

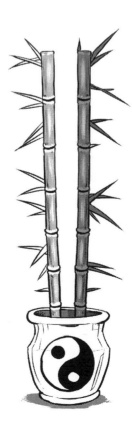

WORKSHEET THREE (1)

1. Which one of the following statements do you agree with?

☐ The three axes of the body divide the body into anterior and posterior halves

☐ The three axes of the body are left/right, right/left and superior/inferior

☐ The three axes of the body create an octahedral structure

☐ Dr Manaka's treatment approach was to balance the energy flow in the four anterior quadrants

2. Pick one correct answer. According to Kodo Fukushima, the goal of meridian-based acupuncture is:

☐ To recognise a disturbance in the *ki* and *ketsu*

☐ To balance front and back

☐ To repair dents and bumps

☐ To regulate qi and blood

3. Pick one correct answer. Kodo Fukushima defined acupuncture as:

☐ The differentiation of excess and deficiency followed by the application of supplementing and draining techniques

☐ The palpation of excess and deficiency followed by stroking and pressing along the meridian pathways

☐ The differentiation of hot and cold followed by the application of cooling or warming techniques

☐ The application of specific techniques on different acupuncture points to relieve symptoms

WORKSHEET THREE (2)

ACUPUNCTURE AS A SIGNALLING SYSTEM.

4. This chapter explains the idea of regulation by using the analogy of a doorbell sending a signal into a house. In the box below, using the same example but in your own words, describe what happens when you ring on a doorbell at your best friend's house, using that as an analogy for acupuncture treatment.

5. Which one of the following statements is correct?

☐ Ontake is a tool that does "stuff" to the body to make it feel better

☐ Ontake engages the body's signalling mechanisms with low-energy stimulation

☐ Ontake is a healing tool with a high-energy signal and is therefore perfect for regulating the meridian system

☐ Moxibustion is especially useful for acute disease

6. Which one of the following statements is correct?

☐ Ontake treatment can be categorised into two primary modes of action: warming and cooling

☐ Ontake treatment can be categorised into two primary areas of action: muscles and bones

☐ Ontake treatment can be defined as the regulation of qi and blood and *kyo* and *jitsu* in the channels

☐ Ontake treatment can be classified as root treatment

WORKSHEET THREE (3)

7. Write down at least two things that you learnt from this chapter in the spaces below. These could be observations, learning tips or any "note-to-self".

CHAPTER FOUR
TAPPING ZONES

THE KEY CONCEPTS OF THIS CHAPTER

- Dr Manaka's frequencies
- Tapping zones
- Intersection points

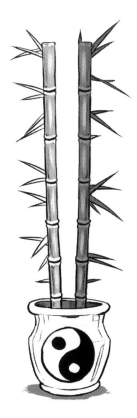

WORKSHEET FOUR (1)

1. Table 1 lists all the channels in the left-hand column. Write down the matching frequency in the right-hand column.

2. Table 2 is blank. In the left-hand column, write all the frequencies in ascending order. Then, in the right-hand column, add the channels.

| TABLE 1 | | TABLE 2 | |
CHANNEL	FREQUENCY	FREQUENCY	CHANNEL
LUNG			
LARGE INTESTINE			
STOMACH			
SPLEEN			
HEART			
SMALL INTESTINE			
BLADDER			
KIDNEY			
PERICARDIUM			
TRIPLE BURNER			
GALL BLADDER			
LIVER			
REN MAI			
DU MAI			

3. How many frequencies did Manaka discover in total?

4. Which frequencies are shared?

5. Which frequency is shared the most?

6. Download a metronome app and set a playlist of all the frequencies, so that you can skip from one to the other with ease.

WORKSHEET FOUR (2)

7. Which of the following are principles for choosing meridian frequencies on an area of the body?

☐ Meridian pathway - choose the frequency of the meridian

☐ Generic frequency – choose a frequency according to TEAM principles

☐ Meeting points – choose several frequencies at intersection points

☐ All of the above

8. Dr Manaka demonstrated the use of the Intersection points as "wild cards" that could be tapped at the frequency of any of the intersecting channels. Answer the following questions in the spaces below.

9. What frequencies could you use on SP 6?

10. What conditions might respond to changing frequencies at SP 6?

11. What frequencies could you use on DU 14?

12. Can you think of any other meeting points you could use?

WORKSHEET FOUR (3)

13. Write down at least two things that you learnt from this chapter in the spaces below. These could be observations, learning tips or any "note-to-self".

PART TWO

ROOT AND BRANCH

CHAPTER FIVE
KYO, *JITSU* AND PALPATION

THE KEY CONCEPTS OF THIS CHAPTER

- More about *kyo* and *jitsu*
- Palpation methods
- The tension assessment

WORKSHEET FIVE (1)

1. Lustre is a term used by blind practitioners in Japan. Which one of the following statements about lustre is true?

☐ Lustre is the term that blind practitioners use for the *kyo* and *jitsu* of a person's voice

☐ It's an indicator of health that can be assessed through palpating the skin

☐ It's the sheen of a person's hair that the blind practitioners sense when someone walks in the room

☐ It's when old people get dry and wrinkly

2. Which one of the following statements about Ontake treatment is incorrect?

☐ To date there is no system of pattern recognition in Ontake treatment

☐ Ontake treatment can be performed with almost no theory, just touch alone

☐ It usually achieves its effect by balancing excess and deficiency in a single channel

☐ In Ontake treatment, palpation is of lesser importance

3. Which one of the following statements about the tension assessment do you disagree with?

☐ Patients like it because it delays needling

☐ Patients like it because they get acclimatised to your touch

☐ The tension assessment is useful as it allows a preliminary assessment of *kyo* and *jitsu*

☐ It includes a tactile assessment of the lustre of the skin

WORKSHEET FIVE (2)

4. Watch the demonstration of the tension assessment using the barcode and write down the sequence in the space below.

5. Differentiate the feeling of *kyo* and *jitsu* by placing the following palpatory findings in the correct columns in the table below.

Cold, cool, depressed, dry, elevated, flabby, hard, hot, inelastic, insensitive, loose, moist, overdeveloped, painful on pressure, puffy, raised, rough, soft, stiff, strong, swollen, tender, tight, underdeveloped, weak.

KYO	*JITSU*

WORKSHEET FIVE (3)

6. Write down at least two things that you learnt from this chapter in the spaces below. These could be observations, learning tips or any "note-to-self".

CHAPTER SIX
TECHNIQUES AND FREQUENCIES

THE KEY CONCEPTS OF THIS CHAPTER

- Rhythm and predictability
- Double time and other variations
- Techniques

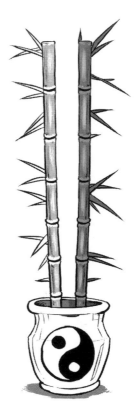

WORKSHEET SIX

20/20 HINDSIGHT

These days, some two years after writing the main book, I've learned to teach the techniques in a different order to the one you see in print. Experience has shown me that it makes more sense to teach them in a certain order and that students grasp them more easily this way. For this reason, I've spent some time in this section to reorder the techniques and I've explained them again here so that you don't have to keep referring to the main book. You can also view them online using the barcodes, which will give you a time-coded link to each technique.

The directions in the main book describe how to apply lighted bamboo on a patient. For learning and practice, however, it is much better to start with an unlit bamboo and a fluffy cushion, as in the video. In training sessions, I call this cold practice. Start unaccompanied, then when you feel confident, turn on your metronome and repeat the technique to one of the lower frequencies. As you get more confident, you can increase the frequency, or try tapping in double time.

INSTRUCTIONS

1. With a piece of bamboo and a cushion to hand, read the description of the technique and try and make sense of it.
2. Scan the bar code and watch the sequence.
3. Practise along to the video until you feel you have a general idea.
4. Repeat steps 1 to 3 later in the day, if possible and again 24 hours later.
5. Practise single time and double time.
6. Light the bamboo and try the techniques on a willing model.
7. Write down any insights or observations that help you.

STANDING
(SUPPLEMENTING)

Place the bamboo vertically on a specific point with the heated end facing down. Leave for four or eight beats and then move it to the next place. This supplementing technique feels very comfortable on areas like the lower Du Mai points or the sacrum. If treating a single point, such as ST 36, stand for four beats and remove for four beats.

This technique introduces the idea that the frequency can be effective even when the bamboo moves at a slower rate than the metronome. Here we are keeping to the frequency but moving only after one or two bars. It feels a bit like moving a chess piece.

Write down any thoughts or observations in the spaces below.

ROCKING
(SUPPLEMENTING)

Rocking is a more dynamic form of treating one point than standing. Hold the base of the bamboo on the point, between the thumb and index finger of your left hand (oshide). With the index finger of your right hand (sashide) holding the top of the bamboo, make a stirring motion, like stirring a cup of tea, so that the bamboo is rocking rhythmically over the point. Rock for one to four bars, taking care not to overheat the point.

Standing and rocking are the main two techniques for treating single points. and it's true to say that they have a very mild effect. Ontake really comes into its own, however, for the treatment of meridian lines and broad areas.

Write down any thoughts or observations in the spaces below.

TAPPING
(SUPPLEMENTING OR DISPERSING)

There are two variations of this. One emphasises the rhythmic delivery of heat to the skin, and the second emulates gentle percussion with the wooden hammer.

1) Hold the bamboo loosely by the unlit end between thumb, index, and third fingers. Place the edge of your hand (the hypothenar eminence) just below the area to be treated, and start to rock your hand so that the bamboo lightly taps the skin. The edge of your hand acts as a fulcrum, allowing the bamboo to oscillate backwards and forwards, and up and down. This is very similar to rolling in Tui Na. The movement should come from the wrist and is always light and supple.

2) Shift your grip slightly further down the bamboo so that you are holding it securely in the middle. With the lighted end about one centimetre above the skin, start tapping while moving your hand up and down in parallel lines. Only the bamboo should contact the skin, not your wrist. This action is reminiscent of the motion used when shaking a salt cellar over a nice unhealthy plate of fish and chips. This technique is useful for tapping on broad areas, such as the upper back and shoulders. It is similar to tapotement in Swedish massage.

For loose, deficient areas, tap the heated end lightly on the skin at the appropriate frequency. For *jitsu* areas, tap more percussively so that there is a sensation of impact with each tap. If you have compressed the plug correctly, there is no danger it will fall out or that loose particles will drop on the skin. If you need to tap even harder, more percussively, see knocking and super-knocking, below.

Write down any thoughts or observations in the space below.

PRESSING
(DISPERSING)

Pressing is a wonderful exploratory technique that gives you much information about the general tone of an area, even as you start to treat it. There is also a variation that can be used in a focused way around joints and muscle insertions.

1) With your palm facing up, place the bamboo flat onto your third finger, moving your second and fourth fingers up a little to create a trough where it can nest. Grip the side of the bamboo with your thumb and rotate your palm so that you can place the side of the bamboo on the area to be treated. Next press the warm side of the bamboo against the muscle in a fluid, repetitive motion. This can be used on either side of the spine on the bladder channel or on the upper arm and shoulder.

2) Hold the bamboo between the thumb and third finger, with your index finger extended across the long axis. With the bamboo angled at roughly forty-five degrees, press down rhythmically into tight areas with the warm lip. This technique is useful for jitsu areas—for example, the medial border of the scapula. It helps to give a slight twist to the bamboo as you press down and then release.

Write down any thoughts or observations in the spaces below.

KNOCKING
(DISPERSING)

Place the hot bamboo on its side on the area to treat, and then tap it firmly with one or two fingers. This safely combines percussive elements of Manaka's wooden needle treatment with the application of heat. Pick up the bamboo after one or two bars and move it to the next point. To increase the percussive element, you can use your knuckle to knock the bamboo, exactly like knocking on someone's door.

This kind of knocking can be used on tight and painful points, such as on the abdomen or in between the thoracic vertebrae. Bear in mind that the longer you leave the bamboo in one place, the hotter it feels, so don't forget to keep the moxa in motion every one or two bars.

Write down any thoughts or observations in the spaces below.

SUPER-KNOCKING
(DISPERSING)

After a few minutes of use, the entire length of the bamboo, not just the smouldering end, becomes warm. A more dynamic variation of knocking is to bounce or "strike" the side of the bamboo with some force, against the skin. Hold the bamboo as you would for pressing, longitudinally in the trough created by your middle three fingers and strike the muscles lightly but forcefully so that you create a percussive wave in the soft tissue.

This again combines percussive elements of Manaka's wooden needle treatment with the rhythmic application of heat and is excellent for softening muscular or *jitsu* areas of soft tissue, such as the buttocks, thigh, calf, or deltoids. It feels very relaxing. This technique is not suitable for bony areas.

Write down any thoughts or observations in the spaces below.

LEANING
(DISPERSING)

This technique comes directly from Shiatsu. In Shiatsu, it is important to apply pressure, not by using the muscular strength of your arms, but by using the weight of your body. In this way, your muscles stay relaxed and open and are therefore able to move qi. Using our doorbell analogy, we can take "moving qi" to mean that we send a signal of relaxation, through our own relaxed state, that is received by the patient's body.

Lay the bamboo flat on the skin and cover it with the palm of your left hand. Now cover your left hand with your right. Lean your body weight down into your right hand, keeping both arms relaxed so that the bamboo is pressed down into the deeper layers. Count four or eight beats and then move the bamboo to the next point, taking care not to overheat the skin. This technique is useful for indurations on the lower lumbar area, abdomen, and the back of the legs and should be followed immediately by rolling to further move the blood. You can reverse this if you are left-handed. The principle is to lean your weight with the top hand into the bottom hand and down into the bamboo.

For example, if you're working on the abdomen, you can lean on a series of points in a horseshoe shape, following the curve of the large intestine. Do several rounds, starting with light leaning, progressing as your patient relaxes and allows you in deeper.

Write down any thoughts or observations in the spaces below.

TOUCHING AND CLOSING
(SUPPLEMENTING)

This is one of the more challenging techniques to implement, and for this reason, although it's a supplementing technique, I've left it until here to introduce it. The movement with the right hand is similar to that of step 1 of tapping, above. Hold the bamboo in your right hand, then place and remove it softly and rhythmically on the skin. As you remove it, slide your left index finger down the side of the bamboo, keeping your palm flat, facing downwards, with your fingers together. Press your left hand softly on the skin. Move the bamboo slightly to the right and repeat. Your left hand "closes" the area treated by the bamboo and pushes or seals the heat in further. Keep moving to the right, sealing in the heat. If you do several passes over the same area, you can monitor the skin temperature changes with your left hand as you press down.

This is a very soft and supplementing technique for *kyo* areas, equivalent to an acupuncturist closing the hole after removing the needle or a very gentle (and safe) version of press moxa with a moxa stick.

This technique is one of the most useful techniques to master and feels pleasant both to give and receive. It's a hard technique to visualise just by reading; even in class, some students find the coordination of left and right hands the hardest to grasp, so try and follow along with the video. One familiar precedent from daily life is the simple action of grating cheese.

When touching and closing in time to a metronome, the left hand should be tapping the skin on the beat, using the same kind of coordination as when grating a piece of cheese with an upright grater. The left hand is like the cheese, and the bamboo is the grater. The left hand follows the metronome and connects with the skin on the downbeat; the right hand pulls the bamboo away and replaces it on the offbeat.

Write down any thoughts or observations in the space below.

VIBRATING
(MOVING)

These final three techniques require mastering the hardest of the frequency variations discussed in the book: the rapid oscillation of the hand, four times faster than the base frequency. It is not as hard as it sounds and has such impressive effects it is well worth taking time to practise. If you are already a musician, you will get it right away.

Place the bamboo flat on its side on the point to be treated, and cover it with your palm. Now vibrate your palm rapidly from side to side, with minimal amplitude, in time to the beat but four times faster. This produces a pleasing, spreading sensation of warmth at the point and can be very useful to deploy on stiff, tight areas or meeting points with unique properties, such as DU 14. It's that spreading warmth feeling that makes me classify the effect of this technique as moving, rather than dispersing. Try it on your thigh and see what you think.

Once again, it is worth emphasising that you need to keep your movements light, relaxed, and subtle. This is not the vibration of a mechanical digger smashing up a road; it is the airy vibration of a dragonfly's wings over a pond.

Write down any thoughts or observations in the spaces below.

BOUNCING
(MOVING)

This technique is only suitable for fleshy areas and cannot be used comfortably on joints or bony areas. As with vibrating, place the bamboo on the point to be treated, and cover it with your fingers, as in light rolling.

This time, instead of vibrating your hand from side to side, oscillate your fingers with an up-and-down movement with minimal amplitude, allowing the bamboo to bounce rapidly on the soft tissue. Once again, this produces a spreading sensation of warmth and relaxation and can be used to release tightness on fleshy areas, such as the calf, deltoid, or waist.

Write down any thoughts or observations in the spaces below.

RUBBING
(MOVING)

This last technique is excellent to use through clothing because the fabric of a shirt or trouser leg enables virtually frictionless gliding over a broad area. Place the bamboo flat on the area to be treated, and grasp it loosely with your thumb, index and third fingers. This time, sweep the bamboo rapidly from side to side, covering a wide arc with each sweep—like the windscreen wiper of a car, but much faster. Hold the bamboo so lightly that it skates across the skin or fabric.

Once again, this rapid oscillatory movement can produce surprising results. Patients love it. This technique is particularly useful on the upper or lower back. It is very useful to use on patients who are still clothed, especially over and around DU 14.

Vibrating, bouncing and rubbing are very similar, in that they are rapid oscillations with differing vectors. You can use rubbing (or vibrating) at DU 14 with great effect, scrolling down through the yang channel frequencies to end the session. Bouncing is not suitable here, as DU 14 is boney.

Write down any thoughts or observations in the spaces below.

RHYTHM CHANGES
(CHANGING THE PACE WITHIN THE SAME FREQUENCY)

I hope you can appreciate from the order of the techniques presented above that you can work with very different tempos, even with the same frequency of beats per minute.

Standing and leaning typically use slow rhythms, staying in place for four or eight beats, while vibrating and rubbing use much faster ones, creating a spreading wave of warmth and relaxation. In between very fast and very slow are knocking, rolling and pressing, which are typically applied on the beat.

This is not just a theoretical observation—it's intensely practical. You can splice fast and slow techniques together, creating light and shade. For example, you can roll around the lumbar area at 112 beats per minute and then stand the Ontake for eight beats below each of the lumbar vertebrae to the sacrum. Or do slow leaning on the abdomen in a horseshoe shape and then roll lightly and quickly afterwards. These slow/fast contrasts feel wonderfully relaxing to receive.

The link above brings you to a quick demonstration of rhythm changes in practice. Take a look at that and list the techniques and tempos used in the spaces below. There's a second worksheet on rhythms overleaf.

WORKSHEET SEVEN (1)

1. Which one of the following statements best explains the advantage of moving the bamboo every 4 or 8 beats?

☐   A change of pace feels relaxing to the patient

☐   It's less tiring on the practitioner

☐   If the bamboo is not moving fast, the plug burns more slowly

☐   Keeping the lighted mouth on the skin for long periods causes a microburn which raises the immune response

2. Which one of the following statements best explains the advantage of applying Ontake in double time?

☐   You can cover a broad area in half the time

☐   A change of pace feels relaxing to the patient

☐   It's more challenging for the practitioner to apply

☐   There's less chance of a burn if the contact time is very quick

3. In the left-hand column of the blank table on the next page, write down all the rhythmic Ontake techniques that we have covered. To start with, try and do this from memory.

In the second column, add a tick next to those methods that are supplementing.
In the third column, add a tick next to those methods that are dispersing.
In the fourth column, add a tick next to those methods that are moving.
Tick any technique that can be used to supplement or disperse.

WORKSHEET SEVEN (2)

TECHNIQUE	SUPPLEMENTING	DISPERSING	MOVING

WORKSHEET SEVEN (3)

4. Write down at least two things that you learnt from this chapter in the spaces below. These could be observations, learning tips or any "note-to-self".

CHAPTER SEVEN
ACTIONS, CONTRAINDICATIONS AND APPLICATIONS

THE KEY CONCEPTS OF THIS CHAPTER

- The possible mechanisms of Ontake
- Actions
- Contraindications of moxibustion

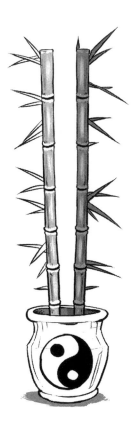

WORKSHEET EIGHT (1)

1. Which one of the following statements is true?

☐ Problems that have been around for a long time are at the Qi level

☐ Acute problems are at the blood level

☐ Chronic problems require moxibustion

☐ Radiating sensations from the wooden needle and hammer indicate problems at the blood level

2. Which one of the following statements is incorrect?

☐ Ontake works at the blood level by draining energy out of the body

☐ The sound of the metronome and the smell of the moxa serve as mental anchors

☐ The smoke may be absorbed through the skin to cause pharmacological effects

☐ The mechanical effects of applying Ontake reproduce effects from physical therapies such as petrissage and effleurage

3. List five actions for Ontake in terms of Traditional East Asian Medicine (TEAM) and give an example of each one.

●

●

●

●

●

WORKSHEET EIGHT (2)

4. List four primary contraindications for Ontake.

-
-
-
-

5. List four situations where you would need to apply Ontake with caution.

-
-
-
-

WORKSHEET EIGHT (3)

6. Write down at least two things that you learnt from this chapter in the spaces below. These could be observations, learning tips or any "note-to-self".

CHAPTER EIGHT
ROOT TREATMENT

THE KEY CONCEPTS OF THIS CHAPTER

- Non-pattern-based root treatments
- Bamboo Max
- Bamboo Mini
- BB-8

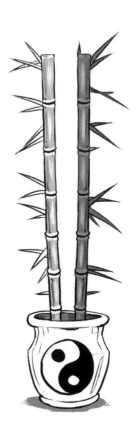

WORKSHEET NINE (1)

1. Which one of the following statements about the Taiji moxa treatment is true?

☐ It's a formula of points that can be used on all patients, regardless of complaint or condition

☐ It's a formula of points that is adapted to each patient, depending on their pattern

☐ It's a formula of points that is given to babies

☐ It's a routine developed by Junji Mizutani for treating all the yang channels with a moxa stick

2. Which of the following is true?

☐ A non-pattern-based root treatment is a term developed by Stephen Birch

☐ A non-pattern-based root treatment can be used on all patients, regardless of complaint or condition

☐ Historically, most non-pattern-based root treatments emphasise the points on either side of the spine

☐ All of the above

3. Which one of the following statements is correct?

☐ Bamboo Max is not pattern-based, so you can take as long as you like with it without risk of side-effects

☐ You should combine Bamboo Max with other root treatments

☐ Duration should always be 25 minutes

☐ Branch treatment may be added to the sequence but only with caution, monitoring dosage as you go.

WORKSHEET NINE (2)

4. The table below shows the tapping routine for Bamboo Max.

a) In the right-hand column, fill in the frequencies for each sequence and treatment area.
b) Can you draw and label the sequence of strokes and frequencies on the model on the following page?

SEQUENCE	TREATMENT AREA	FREQUENCIES
1a, 1b, 1c	Arms (LI, TB, SI)	
2a, 2b	Legs, front (ST, SP)	
3	Abdomen	
4	Side of neck	
5	Inguinal groove	
B1	Shoulder and shoulder blade (GB, SI) If stubborn add TB or LI	
B2	Upper and lower back (BL) Sacrum (BL, DU MAI)	
B3	*Kubi koshi*	
B4	Buttocks and legs (BL & GB)	
B5	Sole and toes	

WORKSHEET NINE (3)

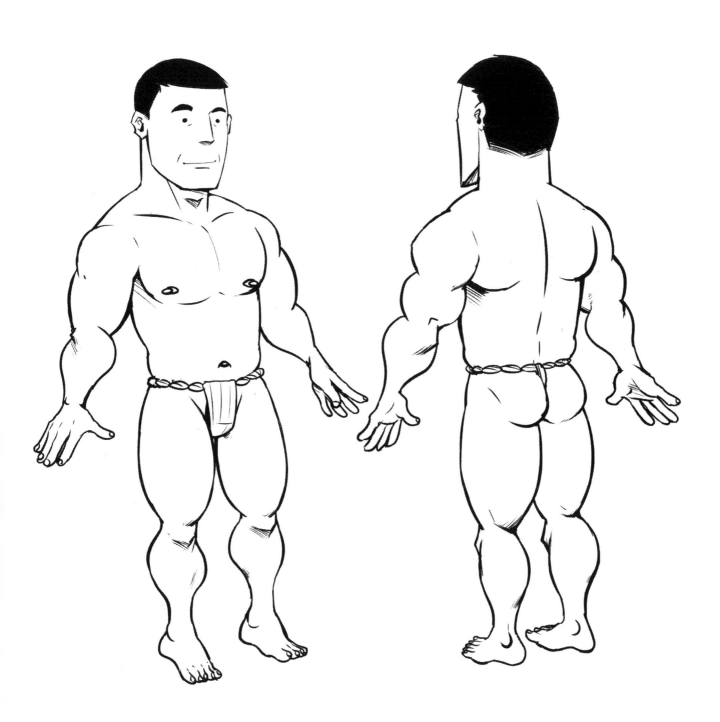

WORKSHEET NINE (4)

FOCUS ON THE BAMBOO MINI

The Bamboo Max is a whole-body routine, but you can take any part of it and do it separately. The most useful part of all is the sequence on the back, what I call the Bamboo Mini. The back is also one of the best places to start practising Ontake. It's a broad region, full of different areas with different muscle tone, skin tone, and temperatures. But, by far, the most important area to consider is the bladder channel, running on either side of the spine.

The Bamboo Mini is a sequence of strokes, working from the top of the shoulders to the sacrum, a useful way to close a treatment. Oguri sensei from the International Japanese Thermotherapy Association in Tokyo says that treating here "wakes up the immune system". Kurakichi Hirata used a similar protocol in the 1930s for patients with anxiety. This sequence is very relaxing. It's probably true to say that I do this on every patient to close the session. But before you try it out on a person, try drawing the strokes on the diagram overleaf.

SEQUENCE

Tops of the Shoulders

1. The shoulders are mostly covered by the gall bladder and small intestine channels, which respond to 120 beats per minute. Tap the scapula and trapezius lightly with the mouth of the bamboo (120). This is a broad area, so it can be useful (and soothing) to tap in double time.

2. Roll the same area, focusing on and adapting your depth and strength to the areas of *kyo* and *jitsu* (120).

3. If the top of the trapezius remains stiff, try rolling at 152. Vibrating can be very useful here. If the trapezius still doesn't relax, treat SI 9, 10, and especially SI 11 in the infraspinous fossa (120).

Back

4. Tap the bladder channel on either side of the spine (112). Some people find working from T1 to T7 first easier, then proceeding to the lower points. Others like to connect the whole back in one long sequence. There's no right way. Just go with what suits you.

5. Roll lightly on *kyo* areas and firmly on *jitsu* (112). Lean on *jitsu* areas for four or eight beats, and then roll afterwards.

6. For urinary, gynaecological, and sacral problems, roll over the sacrum (104). Standing the bamboo on each of the lower Du Mai points for one bar is very relaxing. For example, stand the bamboo below L2 for one bar, below L3 for another bar, below L4 for another, and continue.

WORKSHEET NINE (5)

5. Using the Bamboo Mini sequence on the previous page, draw in the areas and lines that you will treat on the model below, as well as the frequencies for each.

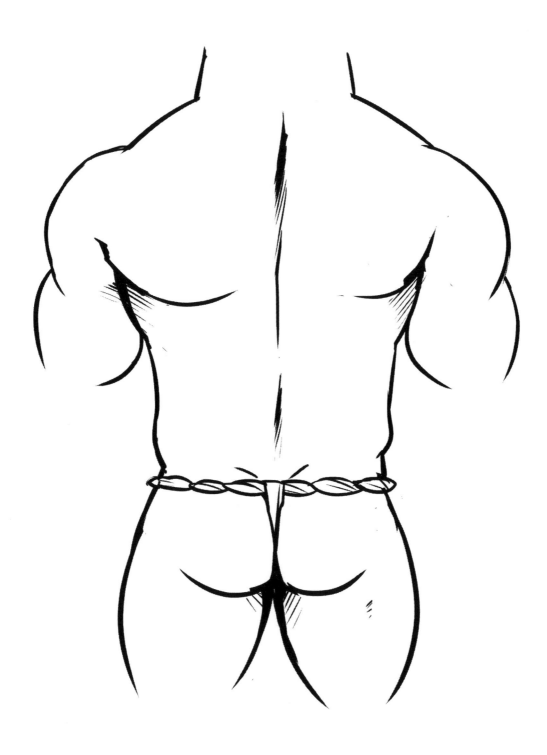

WORKSHEET NINE (6)

6. The table below shows the tapping routine for BB-8.

a) In the right-hand column, fill in the frequencies for each sequence and treatment area.
b) Can you draw and label the sequence of strokes and frequencies on the model on the following page?

VESSEL	TREATMENT AREA	FREQUENCIES
Yin Qiao Ren Mai	LU 5 to LU 9 KID 6 to KID 10	
Yang Qiao Du Mai	SI 3 to SI 8 BL 40 to BL 62	
Yin Wei Chong Mai	P 3 to P 7 SP 4 to SP 10	
Yang Wei Dai Mai	TB 5 to TB 10 GB 34 to GB 42	
Ren Mai	REN 2 to REN 22	
Dai Mai	KID 16, ST 25, SP 15, GB 26	
Du Mai	DU 14 to DU 2, BL 11 to BL 26	

WORKSHEET NINE (7)

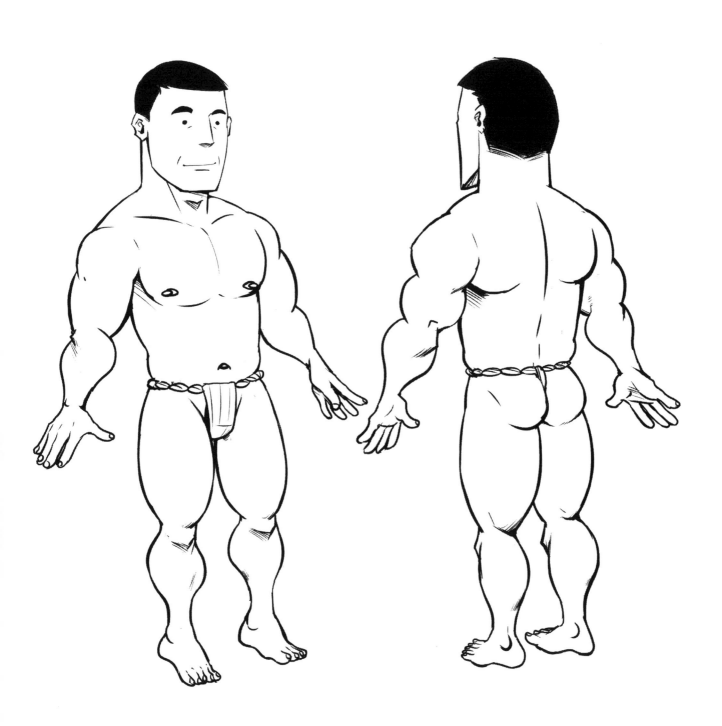

WORKSHEET NINE (8)

7. Which one of the following statements about BB-8 is correct?

☐ This routine cycles between treating yin and yang channels on the hand and foot sequentially

☐ BB-8 treats Dr Manaka's octahedron through the channels related to the master and coupled points

☐ It is a branch treatment that can quickly reduce the intensity of symptoms

☐ To perform BB-8, you tap on the deep pathways of all the Eight extras

8. Write down at least two things that you learnt from this chapter in the spaces below. These could be observations, learning tips or any "note-to-self".

CHAPTER NINE
BRANCH TREATMENT

THE KEY CONCEPTS OF THIS CHAPTER

- Comparing root and branch treatment
- Principles of branch treatment
- Treatment of conditions with Ontake

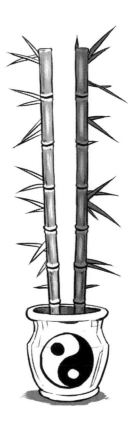

WORKSHEET TEN (1)

1. Which one of the following statements is correct? To date, Ontake has been used in Japan by practitioners such as Yamashita and Shinma as:

☐ A tool to stimulate holographic zones

☐ A branch tool for treating at the site of the pain

☐ A distal tool to treat the root energy

☐ A distal tool to treat branch problems

2. Which of the following statements is true of principles for branch treatment?

☐ Treat locally

☐ Extend treatment laterally and longitudinally

☐ Add distal areas

☐ All of the above

3. Which one of the following statements is true when working up and down a limb?

☐ Treat the *jitsu* areas first, then the *kyo*

☐ Treat *kyo* areas first, then the *jitsu*

☐ Find the areas where there are crunchy crystals

☐ Use distal points then local

WORKSHEET TEN (2)

4. Which one of the following describes the safest option for practice with Ontake on the face and head?

☐ Never use the lighted mouth on the face

☐ Always use the lighted mouth but use caution if it gets too hot

☐ Use a cloth to protect the skin

☐ Be aware that the face has salient anatomy that can protrude into the hot mouth and treat with caution

5. Which one of the following options makes most sense to you? The generic frequency of the eye is:

☐ 112

☐ 120

☐ 108

☐ 132

6. Which of the following statements about the Bamboo Mini do you agree with?

☐ It is the part of Bamboo Max that covers the back

☐ It can be used to treat back pain

☐ It is effective for back pain especially when combined with the leg channels

☐ All of the above

WORKSHEET TEN (3)

7. What is the function of imagining a clock around the navel? Select one answer.

☐ It's a Japanese way of treating abdominal reactions

☐ You can easily remember where you find reactions

☐ It passes the time while you're treating the belly

☐ The Japanese clock is an alternative to the Chinese clock

8. To treat skin lesions such as eczema, which one of the following is correct?

☐ Tap around the edges of the lesion to balance yin and yang

☐ Tap directly on the reddest part to move the blood

☐ Tap distally

☐ Do the Bamboo Mini

9. Write down at least two things that you learnt from this chapter in the spaces below. These could be observations, learning tips or any "note-to-self".

CHAPTER TEN
DOSAGE AND THE GOLDILOCKS ZONE

THE KEY CONCEPTS OF THIS CHAPTER

- Defining the Goldilocks zone in relation to treatment
- Sensitive patients
- Recognising and fixing overtreatment

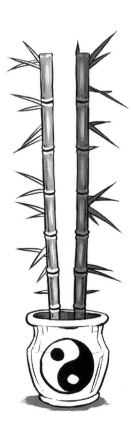

WORKSHEET ELEVEN (1)

1. In your own words, how would you describe the Goldilocks zone for treatment?

2. How does this differ with a sensitive patient?

3. Which of the following patients could you guess would be sensitive?

☐ A child

☐ An adult

☐ A grandmother

☐ A cancer patient

WORKSHEET ELEVEN (2)

4. List three characteristics of a sensitive patient that would warn you in advance that you should reduce your dosage of treatment.

5. List three signs that should make you stop treatment immediately.

6. List three signs of overtreatment that would let you know you may have overdone it last time.

7. Go through your client list from the previous six months and list three patients who are sensitive. Write a red 'S' on their notes.

WORKSHEET ELEVEN (3)

8. List three ways to moderate your Ontake treatment to make it less strong.

9. What could trigger unusual sensitivity? List three circumstances that would warn you that a normal patient could become more sensitive, or a sensitive patient could become hypersensitive.

10. Which one of the following statements do you agree with?

☐ The Jitsometer is a device for judging dosage

☐ The Jitsometer is a thought experiment for assessing the robustness of your patient

☐ The Jitsometer can correct overtreatment

☐ The dosimeter is a device for measuring dosage

WORKSHEET ELEVEN (4)

11. Study the table in the main book on pages 149 and 150 for a few moments and then close it. In the left-hand column of the table below, write down the techniques that you use routinely in your practice. In the right-hand column, write how you could moderate each technique to reduce the dosage.

TECHNIQUE	HOW TO MODERATE DOSAGE

WORKSHEET ELEVEN (5)

12. Write down at least four things that you learnt from this chapter that will affect the way you practise in the future.

CHAPTER ELEVEN
ONTAKE 1 2 3

THE KEY CONCEPTS OF THIS CHAPTER

- Dr Tan's mappings
- Channel pairings
- Treating pain with Ontake

WORKSHEET TWELVE (1)

1. Which one of the following is correct? Treatment with holographic systems is based on the idea that:

☐ The body is composed of smaller and smaller parts

☐ Every part of the body contains the information of the whole

☐ The arm is a mirror of the leg

☐ The body has information that can be decoded

2. Which one of the following statements do you most agree with?

☐ The Back-shu points are a holographic system on a one-to-one scale

☐ The feet contain all the information of the whole body

☐ The ears contain all the information of the whole body

☐ The arms contain all the information of the whole body

☐ All of the above

3. Which one of the following statements make the most sense of the term *isophasal*?

☐ Isophasal refers to all the earth points of the body

☐ Structures and tissues in the body that have the same phase or resonance are isophasal

☐ The frequencies on the metronome that end in an odd number are isophasal

☐ The frequencies on the metronome that end in an even number are isophasal

WORKSHEET TWELVE (2)

4. What is a normal mirror? Pick any correct answers that apply.

☐   It's a holographic relationship between the left arm and the right arm

☐   It's a holographic relationship between the left leg and the right leg

☐   It's a holographic relationship between the left arm and the right leg

☐   It's a holographic relationship between the right arm and the left leg

5. What is a reverse mirror? Pick any correct answers that apply.

☐   It's a inverted holographic relationship between the left arm and the right arm

☐   It's an inverted holographic relationship between the left leg and the right leg

☐   It's an inverted holographic relationship between the left arm and the right leg

☐   It's an inverted holographic relationship between the right arm and the left leg

6. What is a normal image? Pick the one correct answer.

☐   It's a holographic representation of the body on a 1:1 scale

☐   It's a holographic mapping that goes from medial to lateral

☐   It's a holographic mapping that goes from top to bottom

☐   It's a holographic mapping that goes from bottom to top

WORKSHEET TWELVE (3)

7. What is a reverse image? Pick the one correct answer.

☐ It's a holographic representation on a 1:1 scale but backwards

☐ It's a holographic mapping that goes from lateral to medial

☐ It's a holographic mapping that goes from top to bottom

☐ It's a holographic mapping that goes from bottom to top

8. Pick one correct answer. The key to successfully learning mirrors and images is:

☐ Discreet possession of an Action Man or Barbie doll

☐ Memorising key landmarks, then finding the bits in-between

☐ Nodding your head and wrist at the same time

☐ Knowing that the elbows and knees don't change, whichever orientation you use.

9. Which one of the following statements is incorrect?

☐ The area around the eyes of the knee can treat the area around the eyes

☐ The elbow is a hinge joint and can treat the jaw

☐ The knee is a hinge joint and can treat the jaw

☐ The wrist is isophasal with the jaw

WORKSHEET TWELVE (4)

10. List all the correspondences for the elbow, in the normal and reversed mirrors, and normal and reversed images.

11. List all the correspondences for the wrist, in the normal and reversed mirrors, and normal and reversed images.

12. List all the correspondences for the shoulder joint, in the normal and reversed mirrors, and normal and reversed images.

13. Now repeat this exercise for the hip joint, knee and ankle joint.

14. a) How does the idea of a glove puppet help you remember the reverse image? Nod if you understand. Shake your head if you don't.

b) Now put your hand in the air, palm facing forward as if you were waving goodbye. Nod your head again, and at the same time, flex your wrist.

c) Shake your head and at the same time, rotate your wrist.

d) Repeat until you can answer a). Celebrate by making a nice cup of tea.

WORKSHEET TWELVE (5)

15. Which one of the following statements about channel pairings is incorrect?

☐ Internal external pairings comprise one yin channel and one yang, but both on the arm, or both on the leg

☐ Six channel relationships comprise two yang channels but both on the leg

☐ Shigo polar channel pairings comprise one on the arm, one on the leg and opposite polarities.

☐ Six channel relationships comprise two channels of the same polarity, but one on the arm, one on the leg

16. Which of the following steps for Ontake 1 2 3 is incorrect?

☐ Identify the painful channel using the Four Examinations, especially asking, looking, palpating

☐ Check all three channels in the matrix by palpating and looking for reactions of *kyo* and *jitsu*

☐ Pay especial attention along each channel to areas that match according to mirroring or imaging theories

☐ Treat the paired channel at the frequency of the painful channel

17. When treating with Ontake and selecting the side of treatment, which of the following statements do you most agree with?

☐ Always treat on the opposite side to the pain

☐ Always treat on the same side as the pain

☐ Always treat bilaterally

☐ Apply different rules for different pairings but let palpation be your guide

WORKSHEET TWELVE (6)

18. Write down at least two things that you learnt from this chapter in the spaces below. These could be observations, learning tips or any "note-to-self".

CHAPTER TWELVE
BALANCING THE OCTAHEDRON

THE KEY CONCEPTS OF THIS CHAPTER

- Practical applications of Dr Manaka's octahedron
- Treating sore throat
- The Kubi Koshi hypothesis

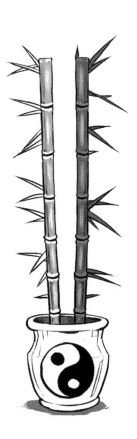

WORKSHEET THIRTEEN (1)

INTRODUCTION AND REFLECTIONS

As I write this section of the workbook in 2021, I have gathered from the lack of questions on the topics of this chapter in the Facebook group and group coaching sessions that it is probably one of the least read and utilised in the book. Probably my bad. After all, I only gave it a two-Ontake rating. Perhaps it was a holographic concept too far? For this reason, I'd like to use this space to re-present the material in the book. There's even a presentation on YouTube to help clarify these very useful clinical strategies (scan the barcode on p.85).

Quadrant theory can be made practical in two ways:

1) Simply tap on the opposite quadrant or quadrants to the problem area. One example given in the book was tapping on a patient's belly, which was icy cold, to release her shoulders, which were super tight—lower treats upper, anterior treats posterior.

2) Tap on paired channels within an opposite quadrant. This is slightly harder to do than with Dr Tan's method because there are fewer pairings in those areas than on the limbs. One example in the book used the kidney channel in the upper anterior quadrants to treat the bladder channel in the posterior lower quadrants.

The principle of opposites is the keystone of all acupuncture treatment; however, there are many ways in which it can be exploited using Ontake. These are so dynamic that I warmly recommend you get a piece of bamboo and try them out.

Although the principles of *kubi koshi* are hypothetical, their applications are pragmatic and clinically very useful. If you take nothing else away from this chapter, use these concepts to treat sore throat!

1. Which one of the following does not comply with Dr Manaka's principle of opposites?

☐ Upper treats lower, front treats back, and vice versa

☐ Right treats left, upper treats lower, and vice versa

☐ Front treats back, right treats left and vice versa

☐ Upper treats back, front treats lower, and vice versa

WORKSHEET THIRTEEN (2)

2. Draw the four anterior and posterior quadrants of the body on the diagram below.

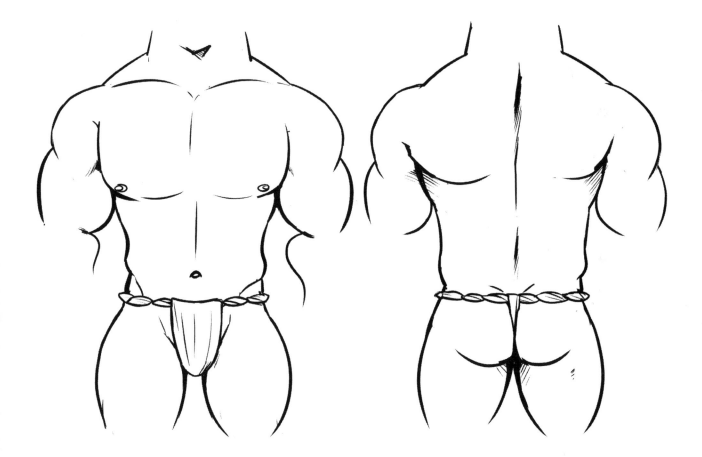

WORKSHEET THIRTEEN (3)

3. Use the diagrams in the book to fill in the matching quadrants in the table below.

QUADRANT	PAIRED QUADRANT
Anterior upper left	
Anterior upper right	
Anterior lower left	
Anterior lower right	
Anterior lower left and right	
Anterior upper left and right	
Anterior upper left & anterior lower left	
Anterior upper right & anterior lower right	

WORKSHEET THIRTEEN (4)

4. Using the channel pairings from the previous chapter: internal-external, six channels and Shigo, answer the following questions:

a) List at least three channels that run through the posterior, inferior, left and right quadrants. Are there any paired channels running through the upper anterior left and right quadrants?

b) List at least three channels that run through the posterior, upper, left and right quadrants. Are there any paired channels that run through the anterior inferior quadrants?

5. How would you treat the following conditions using Quadrant theory?

a) Lower back pain on the right

b) Upper back and shoulder pain

WORKSHEET THIRTEEN (5)

OCTAHEDRON

6. The barcode above takes you to a 45-minute presentation about the clinical applications of Manaka's octahedral model. Scan the barcode to view, then using the information in this chapter and the presentation, describe where you would apply Ontake to treat the following conditions using the *kubi koshi* model.

a) Sore throat

b) Midline stiffness in the back of the neck

c) Mid-backpain on the bladder channel on the right

d) Coccyx pain on the midline

WORKSHEET THIRTEEN (6)

e) Coccyx pain slightly on the left

f) Neck pain affecting the bladder channel on the right

7. Write down at least two things that you learnt from this chapter in the spaces below. These could be observations, learning tips or any "note-to-self".

PART FOUR

BAMBOO SHOOTS

CHAPTER THIRTEEN
INTEGRATING ONTAKE WITH MANAKA'S FOUR-STEP PROTOCOL

THE KEY CONCEPTS OF THIS CHAPTER

- Manaka's four-step protocol
- Ontake variations for treatment at each step
- Introducing the Hirata zones

WORKSHEET FOURTEEN (1)

1. Which one of the following statements is correct?

☐   Manaka's root treatment comprises four steps

☐   Structural problems are the "most significant paradox of the body"

☐   Steps 1 and 2 balance the octahedron at the root level

☐   Counter-resistance stretching is one way to control symptoms

2. Which of the following statements about Step 1 do you agree with?

☐   Ontake can be used together with ion pumping cords at Step 1 to release stubborn abdominal reactions

☐   Ontake can be applied to treat symptoms while the cords are in place

☐   Ontake can be used on the upper part of the body during ion pumping, because the wooden surface will not cause counterflow qi reactions

☐   All of the above

3. If you wanted to relieve stubborn reactions at the right ST 25–27 area by applying Ontake, which one of the following options would you choose?

☐   The associated channels of the master and coupled points being used

☐   The large intestine and lung channels on the upper forearm

☐   The large intestine and triple burner channels on the upper forearm

☐   Gummy areas around LIV 4 and LU 5

WORKSHEET FOURTEEN (2)

4. Which of the following Ontake treatments that we have covered in the book so far could be used as an alternative to ion pumping at Step 1?

☐ Scrolling through all the yang frequencies at DU 14

☐ Releasing the tender points in the clock around the navel

☐ Bamboo Max and BB-8

☐ Bamboo Mini

5. Which one of the following approaches with Ontake fulfil the goals of Step 2?

☐ Channel stretches with Ontake

☐ Bamboo Mini

☐ The upper limb sequence of Bamboo Max

☐ The lower limb sequence of Bamboo Mini plus legs

☐ All of the above

☐ None of the above

6. Which one of the following statements is correct? The key difference between applying Ontake for channel stretching and applying moxa for channel stretching is that:

☐ The practitioner controls when the Ontake is removed

☐ The patient holds the Ontake

☐ The patient removes the Ontake

☐ The patient signals the perception of heat

WORKSHEET FOURTEEN (3)

7. Which one of the following statements about Step 3 is correct?

☐ Manaka used Sotai on every patient as part of his four-step protocol

☐ Sotai is a useful structural adjustment to add at Step 3

☐ Fire needle, *okyu* and Ontake all fulfil the goal of Step 3

☐ If the patient doesn't tell you the Ontake feels hot, it's OK to leave it there a long time

8. Which of the following statements do you agree with?

☐ Hirata Zone Therapy is a Korean holographic system of treatment

☐ Hirata Zone Therapy uses fourteen zones mapped out in six regions

☐ Ontake provides an alternative to the heated needle and rolling tools that were used historically in HZT

☐ Oran Kivity published a terminally boring book about HZT in 2021

☐ All of the above

WORKSHEET FOURTEEN (4)

9. Which of the Ontake variations in this chapter will you consider to adapt to your Manaka practice? Write down at least two in the spaces below.

CHAPTER FOURTEEN
FOLLOWING MANAKA'S TRAIL

THE KEY CONCEPTS OF THIS CHAPTER

- Learning and practising on your own
- Celebrating your achievement
- Questions and "Aha!" moments
- Final thoughts

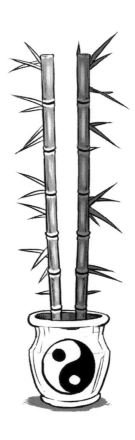

MIKA TAKANO

As the biographical information in this chapter in the main book is more contextual than clinical, I didn't think readers would appreciate or use a worksheet. I am saddened, however, to report that Mika Takano, one of the featured practitioners and a wonderful Ontake clinician, passed away in 2020, a great loss to the profession and the burgeoning world of Ontake education.

So instead, this final section of the workbook advises how to integrate Ontake into your practice.

LEARNING AND PRACTISING ON YOUR OWN

How do you go about integrating all this into your practice? For my part, I always find it's easier to start with the line of least resistance. Start with the easiest things. Start using that if you understood some small part of the root, branch, or pain relief treatments right away.

With time, if you find patients who match other things that you've learnt, use that. Keep reading and keep challenging yourself to bring in new ideas. Perhaps you can start with the symptom relief protocols and later bring in the Ontake 1 2 3 pain relief treatments.

Here are some things you could aim to do:

1) Cold practice on a cushion. Use the barcodes in the preceding pages to go to the YouTube channel and practise all the techniques the book introduced. Practise unaccompanied and with a metronome. Try low frequencies first, then higher ones. Try half time, single time and double time.

2) Try drawing a face and add lines to show where you would tap to treat various conditions such as sinus problems, jaw pain or tired eyes. What other areas or channels would help?

3) Keep practising Bamboo Max or Mini on a family member. The great thing about the Bamboo Max is that it gives you the experience of treating practically every surface of the body: different angles, different textures and different ranges of motion. You will quickly learn to apply different methods in different areas. That's invaluable. And your model will love it!

4) It would be a useful revision exercise to go back to the ends of each worksheet and review your recorded insights and questions. Feel free to share any of these with the Ontake community on Facebook.

CELEBRATING YOUR ACHIEVEMENT

Well, you've done it! Hopefully, by now, you can do some or all of the following:

- Set a metronome to the appropriate frequency for a meridian
- Select tapping frequencies according to meridian pathway, generic frequencies or intersection point frequencies
- Perform the Bamboo Mini, working on either side of the spine to balance the back and calm the mind
- Apply bamboo to relieve various symptoms such as diarrhoea, sinusitis or sore throat
- Apply bamboo to relieve pain using holographic mappings

You should celebrate this achievement by rewarding yourself—you choose how! All that remains in this section is a blank page for you to write down questions or observations. For example, you might be unsure if you got some of the answers on the worksheets right. I'd suggest you also review the observations that I hope you made at the end of each chapter. Those are your big takeaways. And I'd love to hear them!

WHERE ARE THE ANSWERS TO THE WORKSHEET?

No, I didn't forget! I'm just not convinced that putting an answer key in this book will motivate you to root out the information in the main book. If you have some questions you really can't answer, then please bring them to the Ontake group on Facebook. We are a friendly and engaged online community, and we'd love to meet you and hear your questions (the link is overleaf). So please join up and bring your questions there. If I don't respond personally (though I usually do), someone else will.

FURTHER STUDY

There's already one online course of this book, called, as you might guess, *Moxa in Motion*. It's on the Net of Knowledge learning platform. As time goes on, I'll be devising more online and in-person courses, so do visit my author page and sign up for The Ontake Method newsletter, which will have news of study opportunities to come.

NET OF KNOWLEDGE

TEACHING EVENTS CALENDAR

TheⒶntakeMethod

FINAL THOUGHTS

Many thanks to Reza Gunawan in Jakarta, Brenda Loew in Seattle, Jiet Wong in Kuala Lumpur and Bill Deng in Kaohsiung, who encouraged me and helped me to develop and publish workbooks to go with the main books.

It may come as a surprise to readers to learn that this book came after *The Hirata Zone Colouring and Workbook.* That book proved useful enough for me to try and create a workbook for *Moxa in Motion.* I hope both books help you on your Ontake path.

Of course, studying is an ongoing process that is helped by being in a community. Feel free to join the Ontake group on Facebook, to check out the videos on YouTube and of course, to sign up to my website so you can get Hirata and Ontake news and updates or learn about online coaching.

Oran Kivity

Kaohsiung, Taiwan, 2021

FEEDBACK

If you've got suggestions to improve this book, please email me (link below). And if you enjoyed it and found it useful, there's no better way to show your appreciation than by leaving an online review.

You can do this on Amazon or Goodreads, letting others know your thoughts. Thank you!

ONLINE RESOURCES

Youtube.com/theontakechannel

Facebook.com/groups/ontake/

orankivity.com/shop/

orankivity.com/coaching

Email: launchteam@orankivity.com

Made in United States
Orlando, FL
25 September 2022

22769759R00057